Disney PRINCESS

MEGA Colouring

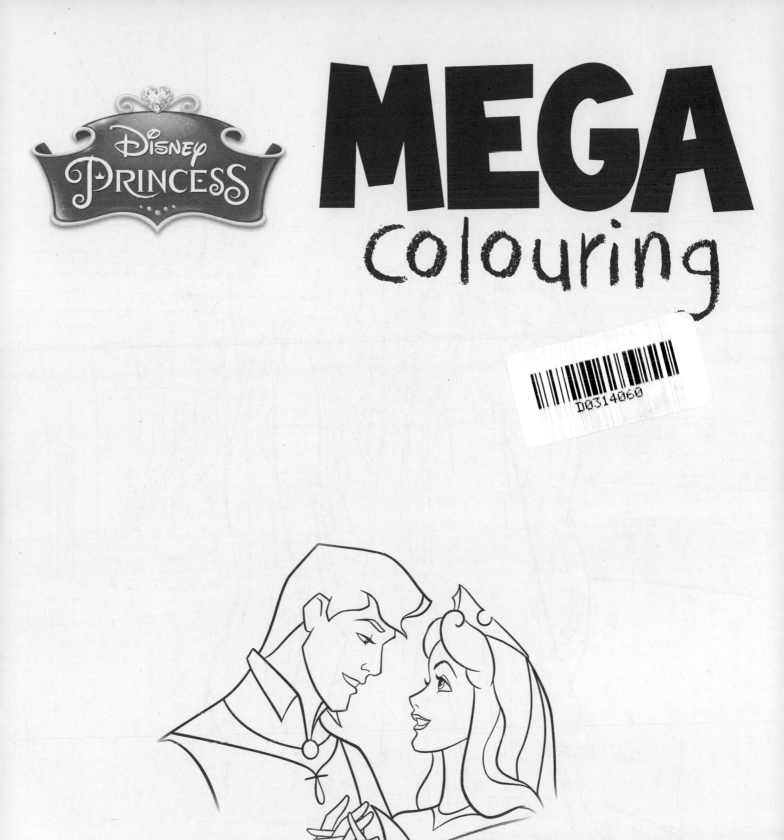

Parragon

Bath · New York · Cologne · Melbourne · Delhi
Hong Kong · Shenzhen · Singapore · Amsterdam

Rapunzel does lots of chores in the tower.

Ariel and her underwater pals enjoy a friendly race.

Ariel loves being a princess in a castle.

Jasmine is lucky to have a good friend like Rajah.

Do you think Aurora likes blue or pink?

Tiana dreams of owning her own restaurant.

Tiana works hard to achieve her dreams.

Belle reads to the children of the village.

Belle likes to ride with Phillipe through the woods.

Cinderella starts the day with a happy song.

The ducks look forward to Cinderella's visits.

"Do you need help, little turtle?"

Merida is the Princess of DunBroch. She loves archery and adventure.

Angus is Merida's best friend.
She tells him all of her secrets.

Rapunzel loves to paint pictures.
They cover the walls of the tower.

The long tunnel helps Flynn and Rapunzel escape.

Aladdin and Jasmine monkey around with Abu.

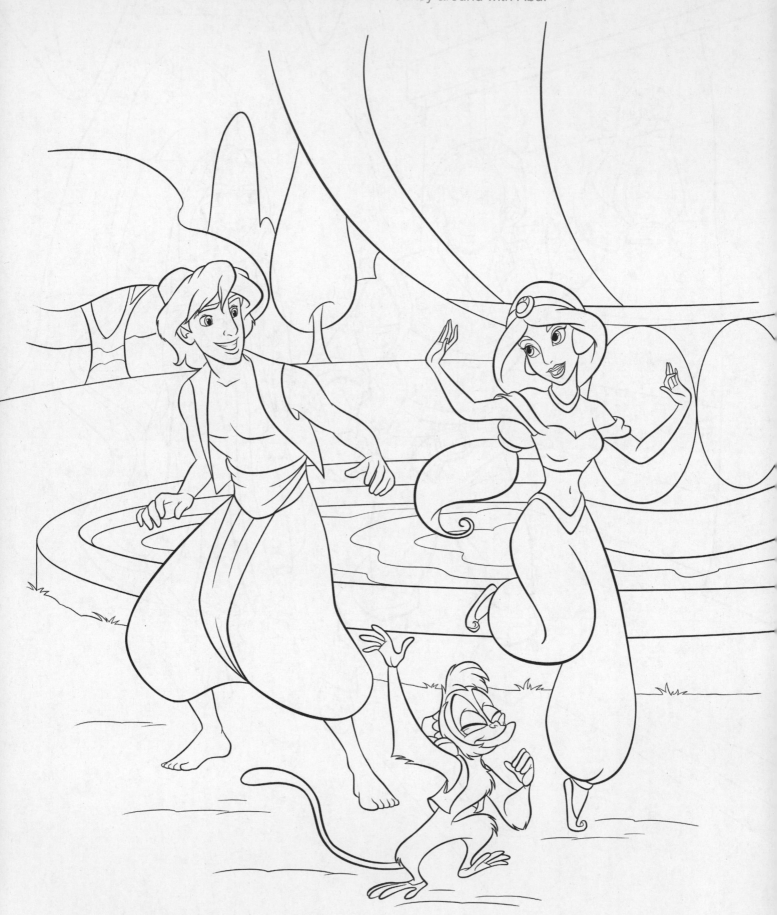

Jasmine and Aladdin try to count all the stars.

Briar Rose arrives home after a walk in the woods.

Aurora adds small candy roses to a birthday cake.

Charlotte lends one of her
fancy dresses to Tiana.

Tiana looks like a princess.

Belle loves her father very much.

Gaston is sure Belle will want to marry him.

Cinderella has made a special treat for Jaq's birthday.

The mice give Lucifer a new look.

The Dwarfs are cleaning the cottage
to surprise Snow White.

The Dwarfs give Snow White
a beautiful sparkling diamond.

Merida loves to explore the
Scottish Highlands with Angus.

Queen Elinor tries to make Merida
look neat and tidy. Merida isn't happy!

Rapunzel helps Pascal recover from their underwater swim.

The little girls are thrilled to braid all of Rapunzel's hair.

Flounder cares very much for his friend Ariel.

It is time to do the shopping.

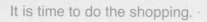

"Don't be afraid. It is only a mouse!"

The squirrels like playing among the yellow flowers.

Using her imagination, Aurora tells a story.

Tiana wishes upon the Evening Star.

Ugh! Does that frog really want to be kissed?

Prince Charming and Cinderella
take Bruno for a brisk walk.

The Fairy Godmother joins
Cinderella for tea and a chat.

Snow White and the Prince take a walk
in the meadow under the moonlight.

Merida hates being dressed up like a proper princess. She can hardly move!

Bullseye! Merida wins the
archery competition.

Rapunzel can't believe her eyes as she
looks in the window of the bookstore.

Rapunzel and Flynn share a quiet moment on the lake as they wait for the floating lights.

Ariel offers Scuttle something
from the human world.

Ariel's family will always love her.

Aladdin gives Jasmine a beautiful new dress.

Let's get ready for a picnic!

Tiana becomes a princess when she marries Prince Naveen.

Naveen and Tiana make a perfect couple.

Belle's love broke the spell on the Beast and turned him back into a handsome prince.

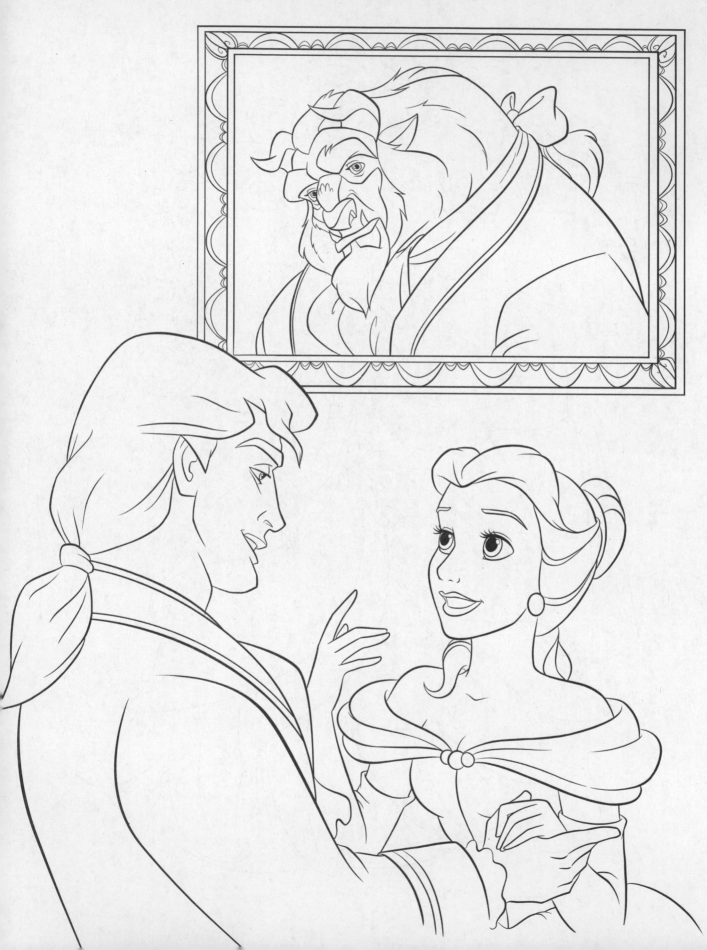

There are lots of things to buy today.

With help from her animal friends,
Cinderella sews a new suit for Prince Charming.

Cinderella's favourite vegetables
are broccoli and carrots.

Queen Elinor wants Merida to marry. But the Princess says she isn't ready.

Rapunzel is filled with wonder as she looks at the floating lights up close for the very first time.

Flynn and Rapunzel launch their own lantern into the sky.

Ariel will never forget her life under the sea.

Tonight is perfect for a ride in
the magic of the moonlight.

Jasmine gives her shoes to someone who lost hers.

Prince Phillip and Aurora go for
a ride through the country.

Tiana looks beautiful in the bayou!

Naveen and Tiana wave as they leave the church.

Belle keeps a diary of her happy memories.

"What do you think we could get
Chip for his birthday?"

Cinderella dreams of the ball and wonders
if she can still dance with only one slipper.

Cinderella gives Major a treat.

The squirrels find a red ribbon for Snow White's hair.

Snow White calls the Dwarfs for dinner.

Everyone is anxious to meet Rapunzel.

As a reformed thief, Flynn sheepishly returns
the crown to its rightful owner.

"My love for you is as big as the ocean!"

You can see the whole city flying
on the Magic Carpet.

Aurora loves listening to music.

This mummy bird has just had babies.

Tiana's dream comes true when she opens her restaurant.

Tiana and Naveen love to dance.

Belle and the Prince have dinner together every night.

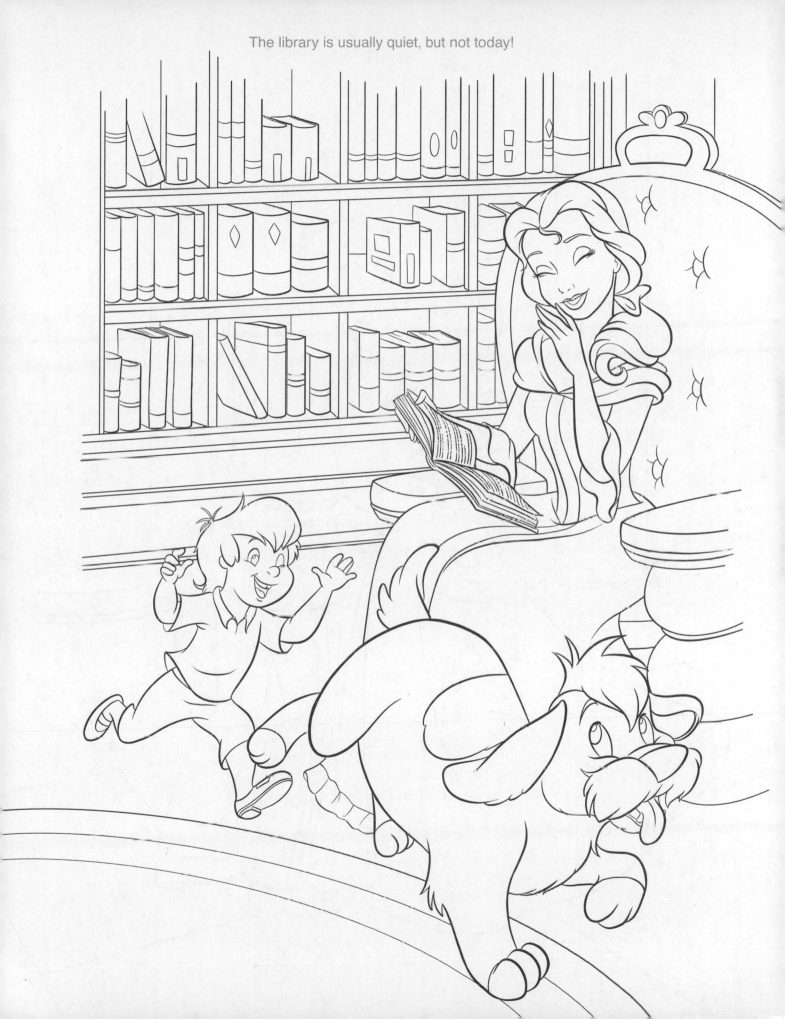

Prince Charming and Cinderella enjoy
an anniversary dance.